Keep Thinking

Graded Exercises in Anticipation and Prediction

Lynn Hutchinson

HODDER AND STOUGHTON
LONDON SYDNEY AUCKLAND TORONTO

British Library Cataloguing in Publication Data

Hutchinson, Lynn
   Keep thinking: graded exercises in
   anticipation and prediction.
   1. English language—Examinations, questions, etc.
   I. Title
   428.2—   PE1112
   ISBN 0 340 36446 7

First published 1985
Copyright © 1985 Lynn Hutchinson

Typeset in 12/16 pt Univers Medium (Monophoto) by Butler and Tanner Ltd.
Printed in Great Britain for Hodder and Stoughton Educational,
a division of Hodder and Stoughton Ltd,
Mill Road, Dunton Green, Sevenoaks, Kent
by Butler and Tanner Ltd, Frome and London

Contents

Preface

The stories in this book have been written in episodes, and each episode is followed by six questions. No literal answers are required. Readers must read between and beyond the lines. They will have to make inferences, discriminate between facts and opinions, justify generalisations, and perceive various relationships in time and space. They are encouraged to make mental images, as well as interpret figurative language. Logical judgments and conclusions supported by argument may be called for. These responses are exercises in anticipation and prediction, and belong to the higher-order levels of comprehension.

The stories develop logically. The nature of the involvement of reader and story is active and creative, and motivation is therefore high.

Reading and thinking, speaking and listening are united in this language activity when the reading of each episode and questions is followed by group discussion, which should lead to further gains in understanding and clear thinking.

This is the second title in a group of three graded books, the others being *Start Thinking* and *Stories for thinking*.

Story 1 The Elm Road Cat

The Potters lived in a small modern bungalow across the road from Mandy's house, in Elm Road. Before that, they lived in Albert Street, where they had brought up their children. Then, when Mr Potter couldn't manage the stairs any more, they were re-housed in Elm Road.

The Potters seemed nice people. No one came to see them, though. All their friends were still in Albert Street. Mandy's mother said it was a shame, moving them so far out of town. But she worked, so didn't have much time to be friendly herself.

Then, one day, Mandy's father told them the good news. He had found a job at last – but it was in Scotland.

1 In what ways do you think the bungalow in Elm Road was different from the house in Albert Street?
2 Can you tell who owned the houses in Elm Road?
3 Why were the Potters re-housed in a bungalow?
4 Why does Mandy's mother think it's a shame for the Potters to live in Elm Road?
5 What can you tell about what Mandy's father has been doing lately?
6 What will the new job mean to the family?

Turn to page 7

Story 2 **The Bar**

Uncle Bob, Aunty Pat and Linda rented a cottage in Wales one summer. They were going for two weeks. Aunty Pat had a sister who lived not too far from the cottage.

'Why don't the children come over? They could stay for a few days,' Aunty Pat asked her sister. All the children thought this was a good idea.

John and Jenny were picked up at the station.

'I hope you've got your swimming things!' Aunty Pat said, 'You'll need them today. Can you swim?'

Jenny said, 'I'm working for my 25 metres badge. John can't swim yet.'

1 What do you think the family was doing in Wales?
2 How do you think Aunty Pat asked her sister when they didn't live near each other?
3 Why do you think John and Jenny thought what their Mother had arranged was a good idea?
4 Why do you think Linda thought what her mother had arranged was a good idea?
5 Where do you think they were going this day?
6 What can you tell about how well John and Jenny can swim?

Turn to page 8

Story 3 **Good Spies**

It was a dark Friday evening. The rain lashed down, and Nick felt cold, wet and hungry. He had been kept late at school. Now he was trying to hurry. The round was always finished long before this time. The serial he was watching would have started.

Only three more houses, he said to himself. He collected the money at the White House, and at The Beeches. Moon Cottage was right out of the village. A light was on, but no one answered. Nick rang the bell again. Then he knocked as loudly as he could. He felt puzzled. The Jeffreys were always in. He thought he could hear noises, but no one answered the door.

1 What is Nick doing this Friday night?
2 Why does it matter if Nick is late doing his round?
3 Do you think Nick needs a bike?
4 What puzzles Nick when no one answers the door?
5 What do you think Nick will do now?
6 What do you think will happen next?

Turn to page 9

Story 4 **The Beach Party**

'I'm worried about Gran,' Mrs Baker said. 'She seems rather depressed these days.'

'Is she ill?' asked Mr Baker.

'I don't think so', said Mrs Baker. 'She wants cheering up more than anything else.'

'It's my fault she never had a holiday this summer,' Mr Baker said. 'I know she wanted to go to the sea.'

'You couldn't help being off work for so long,' Mrs Baker said. 'At least you are all right now, even if we never went to the seaside.'

Ingrid listened to her parents talking. It had been a hard summer for them all. She knew how worried her mother and Gran had been about her Dad. Now there was her Gran to think about. How could they cheer her up?

1 Why do you think Mr Baker thinks Gran could be ill?
2 Why do you think Mr Baker had been off work?
3 What do you think is meant by a hard summer?
4 Apart from illness, what reason does Mr Baker suggest for Gran's depression?
5 What can you tell about the family's feeling for each other?
6 How could they cheer Gran up?

Turn to page 10

Story 5   **Look What You Made Me Do**

Rodney was cross. He knew they would be late for the coach back to school. They couldn't be there in time now, even if they knew how to get there. Not that it was his fault of course. It was David who had lost the map they were working from. He had lost it at lunch-time when they'd had their picnic. Rodney had made it into a paper plane, and David had thrown it into the river. It wouldn't have mattered so much if Rodney had had his own map. It wasn't his fault that he didn't hear properly, when their teacher told them to check their worksheets. In fact, it was really the teacher's fault for not making sure they all knew what they should have with them.

1   Where do you think the boys are?
2   What do you think they are doing there?
3   What would be the consequences of them being late for the coach?
4   Why are they going to be late?
5   Whose fault do you think it is that they lost their map?
6   Why do you think Rodney thinks it is the teacher's fault he didn't have a map?

Turn to page 11

Story 6 The Bird Sanctuary

Mr Butt was very fond of his garden. In the winter he spent hours poring over the seed catalogues. In the spring he started sowing. Young green shoots would show quite soon. Blossom would appear on the fruit trees. From the late spring, vegetables then fruits were picked and eaten till well into the autumn. Then it was time for picking and storing. Even in the winter there were fresh vegetables like sprouts and leeks.

Mr Butt loved all this. He loved to see the plants respond to the seasons. He enjoyed caring for the plants and trees. He liked harvesting the produce at the best moment.

In fact the only thing Mr Butt didn't like about his garden were the feathered pests. With them, it was all out war.

1 For what purpose do you think Mr Butt pored over the seed catalogues?
2 Why do you think Mr Butt sowed in the spring?
3 Why do you think fruits generally take longer to grow than vegetables?
4 Why is the autumn the time for storing?
5 What do you think will be the main differences between fruit and vegetables produced by Mr Butt, and those bought in the shops?
6 What do you think Mr Butt objects to about the feathered pests?

Turn to page 12

At first, Mandy was pleased. She'd never moved before. Then she was sad at the thought of her friends. She would be leaving school, too. What a lot she would miss!

Problems arose when Mandy's father went to his new job. He couldn't find the right place for them to live. It was costing too much for them to live apart, so Mandy's mother said they would just have to go. They would live in rented rooms until they could find a house they liked.

When Mandy's father wrote to say he'd found some rooms to rent, they were pleased. Then came the blow. Pets were not allowed.

'What about Tiddles?' burst out Mandy.

1   Why do you think Mandy was pleased at first to hear they would be moving?
2   Why did it cost a lot for the family to live apart?
3   What do you think are the biggest differences between living in rented rooms or a rented house?
4   Why do you think Mandy and her mother were pleased to know Mandy's father had found rooms?
5   Who do you think Tiddles is?
6   What do you think will happen to Tiddles?

Turn to page 13

The beach was long and golden. The children quickly changed and went splashing into the sea. There were lots of people about. Uncle Bob and Aunty Pat sat on the sloping beach, watching the children. They played in a pool formed by a long bar of sand. On the bar, fifty yards from the shore, the water was only a few inches deep. In the pool it was up to three feet deeper.

Uncle Bob and Aunty Pat felt quite happy. The children couldn't be swept out to sea because of the bar. The bar kept them safe when the tide was going out. But they hadn't thought about when it was coming in. And then the tide turned.

1   What can you tell about the place and the day?
2   Why do Aunty Pat and Uncle Bob watch the children?
3   How does the bar make it safer when the tide is going out?
4   What will happen to the pool when the tide comes in?
5   How can the bar be a danger when the tide comes in?
6   What do you think will happen next?

Turn to page 14

Nick stood on the doorstep and thought. If the Jeffreys had heard him, they didn't want to answer the door. If they hadn't heard him by now, then they never would. He had knocked hard enough. They would have to pay for two weeks next time. He had wasted enough time. As Nick turned his bike round he had an odd feeling. He felt as if he was being watched. He looked back at the house. It seemed quite normal. The only slightly unusual thing was the red estate car parked down the side of the house. The car looked full of luggage. The Jeffreys must have visitors, Nick thought, and they must be having quite a party. As he cycled home, he couldn't shake off the feeling of unease.

1   Would the Jeffreys be expecting Nick?
2   If the Jeffreys had heard Nick, why might they not answer the door?
3   What reasons are there for Nick's feeling of unease?
4   Why does Nick think there might be a party going on?
5   What would make you think there isn't a party going on?
6   What do you think is going on in the house?

Turn to page 15

Ingrid thought about her Gran when she went to bed that night. As she had hoped, in the morning when she woke, she had a brilliant idea. At breakfast she suggested it.

'It's Gran's birthday soon. Why don't we have a beach party?'

'At this time of year?' her Dad laughed. 'You must be joking.' Mrs Baker said, 'In any case we couldn't afford it.'

'No, an indoor beach party. And it wouldn't cost much', Ingrid said. 'Let's make the kitchen into a beach. We could use that sand in the garden.'

'That sand is for the concrete path. I'll get around to it soon,' Mr Baker protested. Mrs Baker could hardly speak.

'Sand? In the kitchen? On purpose?'

1   Why do you think Ingrid's brilliant idea came in the morning?
2   Why do you think the family can't afford to spend much on a trip at the moment?
3   What is Ingrid suggesting they do with the sand?
4   Why do you think Mr Baker hasn't done the path yet?
5   Why is Mrs Baker almost speechless?
6   What other ideas have you for turning the kitchen into a beach?

Turn to page 16

In any case, if it hadn't been for his mother he would have heard. She should have given him a proper clip for his clipboard. Then he wouldn't have been so busy trying to keep his papers in order with a peg. To say that he'd only told her about the school trip after the shops had closed was just an excuse. She should have looked when she came back from her night out. Then she might have found the one he used last time. She couldn't expect him to know where things were kept. Besides, he'd been busy watching television. That was only fair when he'd had to babysit for his brother so she could go out. He had been doing her a favour. Now he was lost and it was all her fault.

1   Why didn't Rodney hear properly?
2   Why is a peg not as good as a bull dog clip for a clipboard?
3   What is the real reason Rodney hasn't got a proper clip?
4   What do you think Rodney feels about how his mother treats him?
5   How do you think Rodney would like his mother to treat him?
6   What do you think of Rodney's idea of fair?

Turn to page 17

The birds loved to peck the pea and bean flowers. They nipped the middles out of the fruit blossoms. There were sometimes no cherries at all because of the birds. When fruit did develop, they sat on the branches and pecked it. When the apples and pears were ripe they would peck the best ones. This caused the fruit to rot.

Mr Butt put thread all over the blackcurrant bushes. He put a net over the raspberries and strawberries. The birds just held on to it. They pecked the berries through it. They even found their way inside it. With the large trees, the birds had everything their own way.

In desperation, Mr Butt decided there was only one thing left to try.

1   What is so bad about nipping the middles out of fruit blossoms?
2   Why do you think the birds do all this damage?
3   Why do you think pecking apples and pears makes the fruit rot?
4   What is the idea behind using thread, do you think?
5   Why did the birds have their own way with the large trees?
6   What do you think is the one thing left to try?

Turn to page 18

'Tiddles will have to go,' said Mandy's mother. 'We have to go to your father.'

'She's not being put down!' Mandy cried. 'I'd rather not go!'

'We'll have to think of something,' said Mandy's mother. 'I don't want her put down either. We'll try to find another home for her.'

The next week was spent in packing, and asking people if they wanted a cat. They put a notice in the shop. No one wanted a cat. 'Kittens are more attractive,' said Mandy's mother.

'Old people wouldn't want to be bothered!' said Mandy.

'Mandy, you've just given me an idea. Don't ask me yet, but there's just a chance we can find that home.'

1   Do you think Mandy's mother is being fair about Tiddles?
2   If they can't find a home for Tiddles, what do you think will happpen?
3   Why does Mandy's mother think people don't want a cat?
4   Why might older people prefer a cat to a kitten?
5   What idea do you think Mandy has given her mother?
6   What do you think will happen next?

Turn to page 19

The children jumped up and down in the water. They waved now and again. The adults waved back. The children fooled around, pretending to be in trouble. They half swam from the water's edge to the bar and back again. After a while they came out. Then they all had a picnic.

After their sand sandwiches, the children wanted to go in the water again. This time they waded and splashed their way to the end of the beach. Aunty Pat and Uncle Bob walked beside them on the sand. Coming back, they noticed the children chest deep in the water, waving to them. They waved back. The children jumped up and down and waved again. Again the adults waved back.

1   Why do they have sand sandwiches?
2   How long do you think it is since the tide turned?
3   What will have happened to the pool and the bar by now?
4   What do you think the children are waving for?
5   Why do the adults keep waving back?
6   What do you think is going to happen?

Turn to page 20

14

As Nick sat down, the programme ended. His sister started to explain what had happened, when Nick's attention was suddenly caught.

'An antique shop was raided in London this evening. Thieves got away with four thousand pounds worth of goods. The thieves were seen heading for Suffolk. They were driving a red estate car, registration number NIC 731 X.'

'That's funny,' said Nick. 'There was a red estate car parked on the far side of the Jeffreys' house. They didn't answer when I went for the paper money but I'm sure they were in.'

'Did you see the number?' asked Joan.

'No,' said Nick.

'Let's go then,' said Joan. 'Come on.'

'Don't be daft,' replied Nick. 'Anyway, I've left my other coat at school.'

1 How do you think Nick feels when he sits down?
2 What programme followed the serial?
3 What do you think goes through Nick's mind when he hears about the robbery?
4 Where does Joan want to go, and why?
5 Why does Nick not want to go out again?
6 What do you think will happen next?

Turn to page 21

Mr Baker laughed again, 'We could turn the taps on, of course.'

Mrs Baker looked even more alarmed.

'We won't need to do that,' Ingrid said. 'There's Alex's padddling pool. He'd love it too. He could have his bucket and spade. I'm sure Mrs Casey would lend us her beach umbrella. We could have a picnic! You said Gran needed cheering up. Wouldn't it be a lovely surprise for her?'

'The kitchen has a stone floor. I suppose it wouldn't do any damage,' said Mrs Baker, looking round. 'We could keep the door to the sitting-room closed.'

'Please say yes,' pleaded Ingrid. 'It would be such fun. I'm sure Gran would love it. She does enjoy a joke.'

1   Why do you think Mr Baker suggested turning the taps on?
2   Who do you think Alex is?
3   What sort of floors would not be suitable to put sand on, and why?
4   Why would Mrs Baker want the sitting-room door closed?
5   Why does Ingrid think a beach party would cheer Gran up?
6   What would be the best food for a beach party?

Turn to page 22

'The coach was going to be outside the Castle at 2.30,' David said. 'You would think you could see it from all round, but the shops get in the way. It's probably up that hill.' He set off with Rodney behind.

'I hope you're right. I don't recognise this,' he grumbled. After five more minutes, David stopped.

'I can see it through the gaps between those buildings. It's right over there. We're on the wrong hill.'

'Now you've delayed us even more. Why didn't you ask the way if you didn't know it?'

A clock struck a quarter to the hour. Just then the skies opened. Rain poured down. In a couple of minutes their clothes were soaked through to the skin.

'Run,' said David. 'And stop moaning.'

1   Why do you think David expects to see the castle from all round?
2   Why do you think David looks for the castle up the hill?
3   Why do you think David didn't ask the way?
4   Why do you think Rodney didn't ask the way?
5   What time is it when it pours?
6   What can you tell about the time of year it is?

Turn to page 23

Mr Butt's family was very pleased with the cat. Mr Butt wasn't so sure. It didn't seem to notice the birds. The birds weren't worried by the cat. They would hop a few feet away if it came near, but there were always dozens pecking away behind its back.

Other cats seemed to appear from nowhere. Next door's ginger tom moved in. It now had a habit of digging holes in his garden. Mr Butt placed sticks round his seed-beds. Then he stretched cotton thread backwards and forwards between the sticks. That should keep the cats out, he thought grimly.

When he saw their cat stepping neatly between the threads, carefully digging holes and tossing the little seedlings into the air, he was very angry.

'That cat is going back!' he told his crying family.

1   Why aren't the birds scared by the cat?
2   Why do you think other cats come into the garden now?
3   Why do cats dig lots of holes?
4   What is harmful about digging holes?
5   Where do you think Mr Butt got the cat from?
6   What do you think Mr Butt will do next?

Turn to page 24

'It's agreed,' smiled Mandy's mother. 'Mrs Potter will have Tiddles until we're settled.'

Mandy's family came back to visit for Christmas. They stayed with relations. Then came the moment Mandy had been waiting for.

'My dears,' Mrs Potter explained, 'I can't give you Tiddles back now. One night last week she woke us up with howling and scratching outside our bedroom door. I didn't think at first that something was wrong. Then I thought it wasn't like Tiddles to make a noise like that. By the time I opened the door, she was unconscious. The house was full of gas. I opened the windows and called for help. So you see, we can't let her go now. She saved our lives.'

1   Why do you think Mrs Potter agreed to have Tiddles?
2   Which moment was Mandy waiting for?
3   What was brave and clever about the way Tiddles behaved?
4   What would have happened to the Potters if they hadn't had Tiddles?
5   Why does Mrs Potter want to keep her?
6   What would you do now if you were Mandy?

The children carried on waving and jumping up and down. 'Aren't they having a good time together?' said Aunty Pat. 'Linda does enjoy being with her cousins.' She waved again.

'I suppose they're all right,' said Uncle Bob. 'They aren't out of their depth.' He signalled to them to come to the shore. Then he realised. 'They aren't playing. They're in trouble!'

He started to run into the water. By the time he was knee deep, a swimmer, hearing loud cries, had picked John up. She carried him to shallow water. Then she returned and led the girls through the shoulder-deep water, until they were safely in the shallows again.

1   What do you think the children try to tell the adults?
2   Where exactly were the children?
3   Why were they in danger?
4   Why do you think Aunty Pat thought they were just playing?
5   Why do you think the children can't make themselves heard?
6   Why does the swimmer help John first?

Joan parked her bike at the side of the road. Then she crept in through the gate of Moon Cottage, keeping in the shadows. She started to feel silly. The biggest crime in the village so far had been stolen milk.

When she saw the car, she realised the play-acting was over, unless she'd made a mistake. She knew she must act fast.

'Well?' asked Nick, as she rushed into the room.

'NIC 731 X,' Joan replied. They stared at each other for a moment. Nick said, 'We'd better tell Dad. Then we'd better phone the police.'

'You paper boys make good spies,' a policeman said later.

'The Jeffreys will want to thank you both when they are allowed home. And I shouldn't be surprised if there is a reward.'

1   Why do you think Joan feels silly?
2   What do you think Joan means by 'play-acting'?
3   Why did Joan think she would have to move fast?
4   Why do you think the policeman says what he does about paper boys?
5   Where do you think the Jeffreys might be?
6   What do you think has happpened since the phone call?

Two weeks later, Mrs Baker and Alex went to collect Gran. Ingrid and her father put six barrow loads of sand on the kitchen floor. Alex's beach toys were spread around on it. The paddling pool was filled with warm water. The kitchen table and chairs had been replaced by deck-chairs, and the umbrella. Flasks had been made. The fish paste sand-wiches were wrapped. There was ice cream in the fridge. The birthday cake, shaped like a life jacket, was on the side.

Ingrid put the borrowed cassette into the cassette recorder. Sea sounds filled the kitchen. Then she changed.

She never forgot the look on Gran's face as she took in the scene.

'Happy birthday, Gran!' they all said. 'And take off your shoes!'

1 Why do you think Alex had gone with Mrs Baker?
2 Why do you think the food and drink had been prepared and wrapped beforehand?
3 Why does Ingrid want a cassette on?
4 Where do you think Ingrid borrowed the cassette of sea sounds?
5 What do you think Ingrid changed into?
6 What expressions do you think Ingrid saw on her Gran's face?

As they ran down the hill in the rain, Rodney slipped. Trying to save himself he dropped his clipboard and worksheets into the swirling gutter. All his work was ruined.

'Now look what you've made me do!'

'What's it got to do with me? I didn't touch you!' David paused as he was stooping to help collect the papers.

'If it hadn't been for you, we wouldn't be here now,' Rodney said bitterly.

'Oh, grow up!' said David, and left him to it.

On his way back to the coach, Rodney shivered. He would have a chill for sure, maybe even pneumonia. After all, it wasn't his fault he didn't bring his cagoule. His mother knew it was getting tight. And anyway, she'd said it would be a nice day for the trip. . . .

1 Why does Rodney blame David for the ruined worksheets?

2 What does David mean by 'grow up'?

3 What effect do you think Rodney's behaviour would have on people?

4 What do you think is the real reason for Rodney not bringing his cagoule?

5 Which of the things that happen to him do you think are Rodney's fault?

6 What lessons has Rodney got to learn before he is independent?

This time Mr Butt returned with a dog.

'This should see the cats off,' he told his family.

It did see the cats off. It did see the birds off. They didn't have a chance to settle to some serious pecking before it was out chasing them. In fact, it was very keen. It would charge up the garden, barking. It chased them through the raspberry canes, which broke. It buried bones under the peas. It dug up new potatoes. When the netting was put on the fruit, it chewed big holes in it. It rolled on the strawberries. You could say it saw off half the garden as well.

Mr Butt built a fence at the side of the house.

'That dog is not allowed in the back garden from now on,' he said. 'I give in. I'm going to turn it back into a bird sanctuary'.

1   How do you think the dog saw the cats off?
2   Why does the dog have a better effect on the birds than the cat had?
3   Do you think the dog is naughty?
4   What effect will building the fence have?
5   What does Mr Butt mean about the bird sanctuary?
6   How has Mr Butt changed?

Story 7 The Stolen Lamb

Paul was the youngest son of a poor farmer. All day the farmer, his wife, Paul and his two brothers worked in the fields near their little wooden house. They chopped down trees and dug up the roots. They collected stones and built walls from these stones. Some fields they ploughed with their horse. On other fields they put their sheep to graze. The family grew only just enough to live on. In the forests surrounding their fields lived wolves. At night, Paul could hear them howling.

One morning, one of the lambs was missing.

'It must be the wolves,' said Paul's father. Paul wasn't so sure. There was no trace of an attack, and anyway, if wolves came close to the farm it was always in winter.

1 What did the family eat and wear?
2 Why did they need to clear the forest?
3 Why doesn't Paul think a wolf took the lamb?
4 Why do you think wolves were more likely to come close to the farm in winter?
5 What season of the year is it?
6 What do you think should be done now?

Turn to page 31

Story 8 Hot Harvest

Ken wiped the sweat from his forehead, and looked at the seven acre field. The combine harvester had finished here this morning. It had cut the stalks a few inches from the ground, taken the rye grains from the stalks, and chucked the stalks out behind as it went. This was the straw, lying on the stubble in rows all over the field.

Ken's boss, Mr Clements, had no use for rye straw and couldn't sell it. It was not absorbent enough to be much use for bedding. It also wasn't good enough for cattle feed. Mr Clements baled all the barley straw, but he burnt the rye straw.

The next job this afternoon was to burn the straw in the field. There was Jim, the foreman, Ken, and a lad who helped at harvest.

1   Why do you think Ken is hot?
2   What is straw, and what is stubble?
3   What sort of farm does Mr Clements have?
4   What sort of bedding do you think Mr Clements talked about?
5   Why do you think Mr Clements bales barley straw?
6   What problem does burning the straw solve?

Turn to page 32

Story 9   **Sophie's Story**

The Youth Club Sophie belonged to was holding a Jumble Sale. Sophie was helping on the toy stall. On the morning of the sale, she and Tina gathered together all the boxes they had been given. They took out the toys and had a good look, then decided on the price.

'What a lot of dolls and teddies,' said Tina. 'They won't sell very well. Here's another to add to the pile.' She handed Sophie an old fashioned doll.

Sophie held it in her hands. A chill went through her. She recognised the doll, yet as far as she knew she had never owned it.

'Where did this come from?' she asked Tina.

Tina said, 'I think that's Martin's box. He was collecting at the other end of town.'

1   Why do you think a Jumble Sale is being held?
2   What do you think Sophie and Tina have done towards the Jumble Sale before this morning?
3   What do you think Tina and Sophie will take into consideration when they decide on a price?
4   Why do you think Tina doesn't think dolls and teddies will sell very well?
5   Why does Sophie suddenly feel peculiar?
6   What do you think Sophie should do now?

Turn to page 33

Story 10 **Piglets**

One Monday in spring, the pigs arrived. David and Tracey watched as the gate was opened. The truck reversed to the opening, and the back door of the vehicle was lowered. Jill and Mary almost charged down the ramp into their field. Mr Sharp closed the gate quickly.

David and Tracey stayed to watch. The pigs rooted around, grunting from time to time. They forced their tough snouts into the soil, searching for roots and grubs. The field was getting more churned up every minute.

'They're looking pretty fat now,' said Tracey. 'I wonder what they'll look like when it is time for them to farrow?'

1 What time of the school year is it?
2 Why did the truck reverse to the field opening?
3 Who are Jill and Mary?
4 Where did the ramp come from?
5 How was the field getting churned up?
6 What is going to happen to the pigs?

Turn to page 34

Story 11   **Clear Cloud**

The alarm rang, and Julie reached out her hand and switched it off. She got out of bed and drew back the curtains. It was still dark. The birds were silent. 'That's peculiar,' thought Julie. 'They are usually making a terrific noise by now. Perhaps the alarm went off early.' She looked at the clock, then checked it with her watch. They both said six thirty-five. Then the bus passed the end of the road. 'The bus is on time,' she thought.

Julie got ready and crept quietly downstairs. She ate a bowl of cereal and in ten minutes was at the shop. Sam was there when she arrived.

'It's like winter this morning,' he said.

'Yes, and it's still dark, too.'

'I was thinking that,' Sam said. 'Yesterday it was light by now.'

1   Why did Julie check the clock with her watch?
2   How do you think she knows a bus passed the end of the road?
3   Why do you think Julie crept downstairs?
4   What sort of shop do you think it is?
5   What can you tell about what time of year it is?
6   How do you explain what is happening?

Turn to page 35

Story 12 **The Return**

'First of all the craft hovered above the sea. It shone and shimmered in the moonlight. The sound coming from it seemed to wake up your body. All of you felt very, very alert. It was as if your body hummed with the sound coming from the craft. Your mind seemed alive and so happy. You felt you could do or be anything. Then the doors of this craft opened. Coloured light streamed out. It came nearer. You knew that it only needed one step – '

Here Amy stopped. She couldn't write any more. Tears rolled down her face. She couldn't take that step. But the others had, leaving her behind, alone and crippled, for the rest of her life.

1 What sort of craft do you think it is?
2 How does the craft attract people to it?
3 Why didn't Amy go with the others?
4 What do you think this craft has come for?
5 What is Amy sad about?
6 Why do you think Amy is writing this down?

Turn to page 36

The next night, Paul said he would keep guard in the field. His mother didn't want him to go, but his father said if he kept his fire alight he would be safe. If he needed help he was to blow his horn. Paul lit the fire between some stones at dusk. His supply of wood was near by. Paul leaned against the wall, wrapped in a blanket. The fire crackled and burned merrily. Paul looked at the flames dancing before his eyes. His mind started to drift away.

Suddenly he was very wide awake. The fire was black and it was cold. Had he heard a noise? Was that a shape he could see sliding into the woods? Without hesitating he leapt to his feet, and plunged after it into the dark forest.

1   Why do you think his mother didn't want Paul to stay out all night?
2   Why should having a fire keep you safe?
3   What preparations has Paul made for the night?
4   What do you think happened to Paul in the night?
5   Why do you think Paul didn't blow his horn?
6   What do you think will happen next?

Turn to page 37

The field was oblong-shaped. It was surrounded by hedges. On one short side there was a road, and on the next two sides there was a three metre wide track, which bordered a wood. Jim got into the tractor, and started to drive round the edges of the field, ploughing the stubble and straw into the earth. The edges of the field were called the headlands. Jim drove round the headlands a couple of times. This left a wide band of bare land around the rows of straw and stubble. This was to act as a fire break when the straw was set alight. Ken looked at the ploughed headlands and wondered if they were wide enough. Then he thought how experienced Jim was, so didn't say anything.

1   On which side of the field was there another field?
2   What do you think was the point of ploughing in the stubble?
3   How would bare land act as a fire break?
4   What would make you decide how wide the headlands should be?
5   Why do you think Ken didn't say anything to Jim?
6   What do you think will happen next?

Turn to page 38

After the sale was over, Sophie went up to Martin.

'There was a box of toys you brought in, Martin, with this doll in it,' she said. 'I wondered where you'd got it from.'

'I remember,' Martin said. 'That came from a house that hadn't been lived in for years – you know, that creepy one behind the wall, the big one, set back from the road. The old woman who lived there died a few years ago. Anyway, it has been sold and it's all being cleared out. There were just a few odds and ends not worth selling.'

'But how did you get the doll?' asked Sophie.

'The woman who cleared out the house gave it to me. Why do you want to know all this?' enquired Martin.

1   Why do you think Sophie wants to know where the doll came from?
2   Why do you think Sophie hasn't sold the doll?
3   Why are the old lady's things only being cleared out now?
4   What do you think has happpened to most of the things in the house?
5   What would you think if you were Martin?
6   What do you think Sophie will do next?

Turn to page 39

Two shelters had been made for the pigs. About 30 centimetres from the ground were rails running the length of the shelter. These were about half a metre from the sides. The adult pigs couldn't get under them, but the little pigs could. Tracey and David saw for themselves later how important these creep rails were.

The first sow to farrow was Mary. Sixteen piglets were born, one after another. As soon as they were born they staggered to their feet. Mary licked them clean, and then they searched her body until they found a teat. As there were more piglets than teats there was a struggle right from the beginning.

1 What do the creep rails do?
2 Can you think why it is important to the farmer to have creep rails?
3 Why do you think the piglets try to walk as soon as they are born?
4 What is the piglets' first food?
5 What do you think the struggle is for?
6 How do you think the struggle will end?

Turn to page 40

Julie kept expecting a storm. By the time she had finished her round the sky was a little lighter. There was still no thunder or lightning or rain.

'Have you noticed how dark it is?' Julie asked her mother, when she went home for her proper breakfast.

'It is rather overcast. Still, I expect it will improve later,' her mother said.

'It's very cold,' Julie said. 'There's been a hard frost.'

'You must still expect frosts in May. I hope your Father's potatoes and tomatoes are all right.'

The sky was greyer by the time Julie reached the bus stop. Car headlights made the frost sparkle on the trees. She looked down and saw a small bird. It was very cold and very stiff.

1   Why do you think Julie expected a storm?
2   Why do you think Julie has two breakfasts?
3   Why do you think Julie is more concerned about the weather than her mother is?
4   Why is Julie's mother worried about potatoes and tomatoes?
5   What does Julie's father do for a hobby?
6   What do you think has happened to the bird?

Turn to page 41

There was a knock at the door. A policeman entered.

'I wondered if you'd finished that report yet, Miss,' he said.

'Almost,' said Amy, drying her eyes. She finished it. 'I don't suppose there's any news, is there?' she asked.

'Nothing, I'm afraid, Miss. It seems your boat was the only one in the area at the time you say this – er – craft appeared. Of course, we could only search for your uncle and his family after you'd been found, and you'd been drifting for a while it seems.'

'They've gone – you won't find them! They went off in a space craft. I saw them go! They'll be in another world by now.'

'Yes, Miss. That's what I'm afraid of. You should have some rest now. I'll tell Matron you're resting, on my way out.'

1   What do you think the report is for?
2   What news is Amy hoping for?
3   How and where do you think Amy has been living till now, and why?
4   Where do you think Amy is now?
5   Why couldn't the police search until after Amy has been found?
6   What do you think the policeman thinks has happened to them?

Turn to page 42

Paul heard twigs cracking ahead, and at first didn't have too much difficulty in keeping up with the sounds. As he went deeper into the dark forest he found it harder to follow. He had never needed to come this far into the woods before. After a few more minutes, when he stood and listened there was no sound to be heard. Looking round he knew he had lost more than the chase. He turned round and tried to make his way in the direction he thought was homeward.

A sudden noise made him halt. He could hear yapping. It seemed to be coming from under his feet. He bent down, and could just make out a hole in front of him. Stuck in the hole were what looked like two grey puppies.

1   Why do you think Paul found it fairly easy to follow at first?
2   What do you think is making the sounds?
3   What do you think Paul has needed to come into the woods for before now?
4   What else did Paul lose, apart from the chase?
5   What do you think is in the hole?
6   What would you do now if you were Paul?

Turn to page 43

The wind was blowing down the field and over the road. Jim set alight the first row of straw parallel to the road. As the straw blazed up, Ken and Malcolm spread the burning bits along the row with pitchforks. The flames burnt towards the headland, then, after a while, went out. More straw was set alight about a metre behind the first. It burnt towards the burnt part and went out.

After this had been done twice more, Jim sent Malcolm round to the other side. At his signal, Ken and Malcolm ran up the long sides of the field, lighting the ends of the rows. This was to keep a burnt out part at the edge when the middle burned.

Then, as they reached the last row, the wind changed.

1   How do you think Ken finds out where the wind is coming from?
2   Why do you think Ken needs to know the wind direction?
3   Why does the fire burn out at the headland?
4   Why do you think they want a burnt out part at the edges for when the middle burns?
5   Why do you think it matters that the wind has changed?
6   What do you think will happen now?

Turn to page 44

Sophie found out from Martin where the person who cleared out the house lived.

For a few days she did nothing about it. She looked at the doll from time to time. Sometimes it just looked like a rather worn doll. At other times it seemed to mean something to her. She would seem to be on the brink of remembering, but then the feeling would slip away.

She asked her parents if they had seen it before, but they hadn't.

Then, one Saturday, she found herself at the entrance of the drive leading to the big house.

It was not as she remembered it. Trees had been felled, weeds cut down, flower beds cleared. When she crept down to the curve of the drive she could see the house sparkling in its new paint. No memories were stirred by what she saw.

1 Why do you think Sophie found out the address of the person who cleared out the house?
2 Why do you think she didn't go straight away to see her?
3 How do you suppose Sophie found herself at the entrance to the big house?
4 What can you tell about how it used to look?
5 Why do you think no memories are stirred?
6 What do you think Sophie will do now?

Turn to page 45

Just as Mary finished farrowing, Jill started. She only had six piglets, but they were all bigger than Mary's. Mary's piglets were all sizes. They squealed and trod on each other trying to find a teat and hold on to it. Tracey and David couldn't stop looking.

Then they saw Mary heave herself to her feet, and go to the troughs for food and water. When she returned to the shelter she flopped down. There were squeals from the piglets as her great weight came down on top of them. They wriggled out under the creep rail. The children were horrified to hear one piglet squeal pitifully and then grow quiet under the weight of its mother.

1 What do you think feeding time was like with Jill's piglets?
2 Which of Mary's piglets are most likely to succeed in holding on to a teat?
3 What is likely to happen to the others?
4 Why do you think Tracey and David couldn't stop looking?
5 Why did the piglets wriggle under the creep rail?
6 Why do you think the squealing piglet grew quiet?

Turn to page 46

By noon it was light enough for cars to be driven with only sidelights on. At four o'clock headlights had to be used again. The frost didn't thaw all day.

'What has happened?' Julie asked her mother when she got home. 'Why is it winter in May?'

They switched on the television news. They heard that the whole country had been plunged into winter conditions. Satellite pictures did not show the dense cloud cover the weather men expected. It seemed that as yet no one could explain what was happening.

The weather remained the same. Night lasted sixteen hours. Electric lights burned all the time. Farmers said their crops were dying. Nature lovers said young animals and birds were dying by the thousand.

1   What effect will these conditions have on the cost of living?
2   Why do you think the weather men expected to see clouds on the satellite pictures?
3   Why are the crops dying?
4   What would be the long-term effects of crops dying now?
5   Why are young birds and animals dying in such large numbers?
6   What would be the long-term effects of young animals and birds dying?

Turn to page 47

In another world, Amy's uncle, aunt and cousin had almost forgotten their time on earth. Stripped of their earthly bodies, their minds grew so that they knew all the secrets of the universe. The time came for their knowledge to be put to use. James, who had been closest to Amy, was drawn back to Earth again. He wished to be near her. This was possible, providing he used a different form. All memories of his time on Earth and in the other world would of course be forgotten.

So it was that 'Jimmy' arrived at the children's home. It seemed he had been lost, or left, in a strange city and was without a friend or relation in the world.

1   Why do you think people arriving in the other world forget where they came from?
2   Why do you think James chooses to return to Earth?
3   What do you think is meant by putting knowledge to use?
4   What does the fact that James chooses Earth imply about the others' choices?
5   What will Jimmy know about himself and who he is?
6   What do you think will happen next?

Turn to page 48

'Are you lost? Do you need saving?' Paul said to them, reaching in his hands to stroke them.

'Ow!' he cried. Paul guessed the little cubs were hungry. He still had the bag across his shoulders with the food his Mother had provided. In it he found some goat's cheese and some bread, which he broke into pieces and fed to the cubs. They took it fearlessly from his hands.

Then came a deep, warning growl. Paul felt icy shivers go up his back. He froze, bent over the hole with his hands full of food. A female wolf appeared on the other side of the hole. She looked at him, then leapt down to her cubs.

Then she sprang out of the hole, and, exactly like a dog, told him to follow.

1   What do you think the cubs are doing in the hole?
2   Why does Paul think the cubs are hungry?
3   Why does Paul have food with him?
4   Why aren't the cubs frightened of him?
5   Why do you think the wolf doesn't attack Paul?
6   How does Paul know he is supposed to follow?

Turn to page 49

The fire swept across the field towards Ken, and the air was scorching hot. The flames grew higher. Where the headland had been ploughed, there were still bits of straw and stubble in the earth. The fire was creeping across the headland on these bits of straw. Jim and Ken were helpless for a moment. It was too late to make the headland any wider. Risking the heat, they stamped out the flames as they spread. They were driven back when the flames leapt right over the headland to touch the hedge. Because of the dry summer, the hedge caught alight quickly. On the other side of the hedge was a track they'd been using all summer. It was littered with straw from the combine and trailers. Then there was the wood.

1   Where do you think Malcolm was when the wind changed?
2   How were Ken and Jim trying to control the fire at first?
3   How do you think the fire reached the hedge?
4   How do you think the fire will spread from the hedge?
5   How do you think Ken and Jim will try to stop the fire reaching the wood?
6   What do you think will happen next?

Turn to page 50

Sophie found the front door, and knocked. The door opened before she had time to change her mind. Sophie told the woman about the doll. 'I just felt I'd seen it before,' she said. 'I wondered if you knew anything about it. Perhaps you know whose it was?'

The woman asked her in, and told Sophie she'd been Mrs Ridley's housekeeper for seven years before her death.

'She was a strange lady,' said Mrs Pearson. 'She insisted that I kept the children's rooms just as they must have been. I knew she'd had a son and a daughter, and the son was killed as a boy, but I don't know what happened to the daughter. She was never mentioned and she never visited. I think there'd been a row. There was a portrait of her in the dining-room.'

1   Why might Sophie have changed her mind?
2   What is Sophie hoping to find out?
3   What do you think is strange about Mrs Ridley?
4   Why do you think Mrs Ridley might not want to talk about her daughter?
5   Why do you think Mrs Ridley kept a portrait of her daughter?
6   What do you think will happen next?

Turn to page 51

The next time Mary stood up, a small, white, lifeless form could be seen on the ground. Mr Sharp removed it while Mary was feeding at the trough. He tried putting some of Mary's smallest piglets in with Jill. She wouldn't have anything to do with them and drove them away.

The next morning, Tracey and David counted only 14 piglets. Another small body was found.

Tracey and David were surprised to see how much the larger piglets had grown in a day. The two smallest ones seemed about the same. Mr Sharp didn't hold out much hope for them. Every day the others grew larger and stronger, while Bill and Ben grew thinner and weaker. Then, one day, Bill died.

1   What had happened to the squealing piglet?
2   Why did Mr Sharp remove it while Mary was feeding?
3   Why did Mr Sharp put some of Mary's piglets in with Jill?
4   Why do you think Jill drove them away?
5   Why did Bill die?
6   What do you think will happen to Ben?

Turn to page 52

When power failures started to occur, the whole country started to panic. All the news programmes were full of the crisis. Scientists agreed that something was blocking out the sun's rays. They said it was as if a nuclear bomb had been dropped. The dust from such an explosion would block out the sun's rays over large areas of the world. This dust would spread around the planet. But this was not a nuclear winter. No dust clouds could be found. There was no doubt, though, that the winter was spreading. Reports from warmer countries told of the even worse effects of sudden darkness and cold.

Then, a month after it started, all the news programmes were full of hope. The substance of which the clear cloud was made had been found.

1   Why do you think there are power failures?
2   Why do you think people started to panic?
3   What is a nuclear winter?
4   How do you think dust would spread around the planet?
5   Why would the effects of this winter be worse in warmer countries?
6   What effects can you imagine of winter coming to a warmer country?

Turn to page 53

Amy often thought that Jimmy's arrival was a turning point for her. She had been very sad and depressed for a long time. Losing two families and the use of one leg was a lot to cope with in just thirteen years.

Then came Jimmy. For a start he had a sort of chuckling laugh that no one could resist. Adults and children alike couldn't help joining in. People liked to be in his company. It wasn't that he was very interesting or could tell funny stories. He was just nice to be with. When Amy felt left out of things, as she often was, and her feelings were hurt, just chatting with Jimmy seemed to dissolve the bad feelings before they did any harm. She always felt better for being with him.

1   How does Jimmy make Amy's life turn round?
2   Why do people like Jimmy?
3   Why do you think Amy was often left out of things?
4   What do you think the bad feelings were?
5   What harm can bad feelings do?
6   Is Jimmy unusual?

Turn to page 54

Paul followed the wolf. She stopped from time to time. Paul had no idea where they were. After what seemed ages, the trees started to thin out. At the edge of a clearing, the wolf stood still. Paul could just make out a shelter. Smoke came from the roof, and he could hear voices and laughter inside. Paul stealthily crept up, and through a crack he could see two men. They were lying on some skin rugs. Over the fire was a cooking pot. On the floor he could see the skin of a lamb. A blood-stained knife lay on the table.

Again the wolf led the way. As Paul went, he snapped off branches here and there. It wasn't long before they were at the edge of the forest.

1   Why do you think Paul followed the wolf?
2   Why does the wolf stop from time to time?
3   What had happened to the lamb?
4   Why do you think Paul didn't challenge the two men?
5   Why do you think Paul snapped off branches?
6   What do you think Paul will do now?

Turn to page 55

Malcolm appeared down the track. He'd had to go round the blazing field. As he joined them, the fire started to creep across the track on the straw. Jim sent him for some sacks from a nearby barn. Ken and Jim started stamping. While they were stamping out the flames in one place, they were creeping across the track somewhere else.

Malcolm soon returned with the sacks. All three then beat and stamped on the flames. It seemed to go on for ever. The hairs on Ken's arms were singed. His legs and arms ached with the stamping and beating. The smoke hurt his eyes, and the heat was more than he felt he could bear.

An hour later they were still at it.

1   Why had Malcolm taken so long to come?
2   What does stamping and beating do?
3   Why do you think Jim doesn't send for help?
4   Would you say the fire was under control yet?
5   What makes the men keep at it for so long?
6   What do you think of their action?

Turn to page 56

Mrs Pearson continued. 'Yet after Mrs Ridley died, no relatives could be found. Maybe her daughter had died abroad, or she might have changed her name, and never knew about her mother's death. That's why the house was left so long, while they searched. Fancy being left a house and not knowing about it! Anyway, dear, I reckon that's where the doll came from. It was Mrs Ridley's daughter's doll. Florence her name was, that was what the notice in the newspapers said.'

Sophie thanked Mrs Pearson and set off home. Florence Ridley, Florence Ridley, she kept saying to herself. There *was* something about it.

It had been a fruitful day. She could now pass the entrance to the drive whenever she liked. She knew more about the doll. But she still couldn't account for her strange feelings.

1 Why do you think Mrs Pearson suggests that the daughter might have died abroad rather than in this country?
2 How and why could the daughter have changed her name?
3 Why has it taken so long to sell the house?
4 Who do you think has done the searching, and how could they have done it?
5 Why do you think Sophie feels differently about the old house?
6 How do you account for Sophie's strange feelings?

Turn to page 57

'Can we take Ben out and feed him ourselves?' asked David.

'It doesn't usually work,' said Mr Sharp. 'The piglet isn't weaned. It should have milk till it's ten weeks old. Even if you manage to keep it alive, when it goes back it is very likely to become ill, or be rejected by its mother and the others. And we haven't got the space to rear it separately.'

'If we leave Ben, he will definitely die,' said David. 'If we take him out he has a chance of living. If he lives, you'll be glad.'

'And we don't mind the trouble,' said Tracey. 'He couldn't help being born small.'

1   Why do you think the children want to look after the piglet?
2   What would they need to feed the piglet on?
3   Why do you think there are likely to be problems if they try to return the piglet to the litter?
4   Why should Mr Sharp be glad if Ben lives?
5   What does Tracey mean about him being born small?
6   How would you look after a three-week-old piglet?

Turn to page 58

After that, the hunt was on. All over the world scientists were busy trying to find a substance which would break up the clear cloud. While this was going on, winter still spread. The countries which it had not yet reached tried to prepare. Weather men studied the wind patterns in even more detail.

Then a breakthrough was announced. Safety tests were being carried out on a new substance. If it passed them, then planes would be packed with crystals made from this new chemical. They would fly as high as possible and then scatter the crystals on to the clear cloud.

The world waited.

Launch day was announced.

Julie was among the many who looked at the dark sky a hundred times that day.

1   Why do you think the whole world was involved in the hunt?
2   How would a country prepare for this winter?
3   Why do you think the weather men studied the wind patterns in even more detail?
4   What safety tests should be carried out, do you think, before putting the new chemical into the air?
5   If it is successful, how do you think the crystals will work?
6   What other important question about the clear cloud has not yet been found out?

Turn to page 59

There was only one person who objected to Jimmy. This was Mike, and he was in the same class at school. He sneered at him for not having parents. He taunted him because he lived in a home. Only if he could make someone laugh at Jimmy's expense, was Mike satisfied.

Mike, of course, was not popular. People were afraid of him, and tried not to provoke him. But he was not liked. Jimmy was, and Mike minded. He dreamed of getting the better of Jimmy in some way.

It was Amy, reaching for her fallen crutch, who saw Mike take money from Linda's desk and slide it into Jimmy's. But no one saw the foot that Mike shot out, tumbling Jimmy down the main hall stairs.

1   Why do you think Mike doesn't like Jimmy?
2   How do you think Jimmy would react to Mike's taunts?
3   What was Mike hoping to do by putting a purse in Jimmy's desk?
4   What do you think Amy would do when she saw Mike put the money in Jimmy's desk?
5   Why do you think Mike trips Jimmy?
6   What do you think will happen next?

Turn to page 60

Paul stopped and looked at the wolf. He bowed his head to her. She looked at him steadily for a moment, and then melted into the blackness of the wood again. Paul knew where he was now, and made for home.

His brothers went for some neighbours. Paul led eight men back through the woods at dawn. He was ordered to wait at the edge of the clearing, but there was no fight. The two thieves, woken from their sleep by eight angry men, were only too glad to leave peacefully, at once, without packing. The men destroyed the shelter, shared out the skins and other items and returned home.

Life went on as before. The thieves were never seen again, and neither was Paul's wolf. But Paul never felt quite the same about wolves after that.

1   Why do you think Paul bowed to the wolf?
2   Why do you think the neighbours were called in?
3   How was Paul able to guide them to the shelter?
4   Why do you think Paul had to wait at the edge of the clearing?
5   Why do you think the men destroyed the shelter and took the things?
6   How do you explain what happened?

At last, the flames started to lose their strength and heat. Working was slightly more comfortable now, even though they were all on the point of exhaustion. But still the fire tried to reach the wood. Still they stamped out the creeping flames. Still pieces of straw flared.

By dusk the fire was almost burnt out.

'That was a close thing,' said Jim. Ken said nothing. He knew how it would have been for Jim if they'd had to call the Fire Brigade, and Mr Clements had been fined. Ken thought Jim might not take so many short cuts to get a job done another time. But this time Ken knew that they had been very lucky.

1   For how long do you think the men worked without a break?
2   Why do you think Jim didn't send for the Fire Brigade?
3   Do you think he should have done so?
4   How do you think it would have been for Jim if Mr Clements had been fined?
5   Why do you think the fire went out of control?
6   What lessons do you think Ken has learned?

Although she couldn't explain things, Sophie felt better. In time she slowly stopped thinking about it.

Time passed. A couple of years later she left school. She then received the greatest shock of her life. Her parents told her she was adopted. They said they'd meant her to grow up knowing it, but it hadn't been necessary when she was very small. After that it seemed too late. They'd decided to tell her when she was grown up.

Although Sophie was happy in her family, she wanted to find out where she really came from. The next two years were very unsettling. When she was eighteen, at last she found out her natural mother's name. It wasn't a surprise. At last she had an explanation, of sorts, for her strange feelings.

1 Why is Sophie shocked at the news of her adoption?
2 What do the parents mean about it seeming too late to tell her she was adopted?
3 What do you think her mother's name is?
4 Why do you think Sophie isn't surprised?
5 How do you explain Sophie's strange feelings now?
6 What do you think could have happened to Sophie's natural mother to explain how Sophie came to be adopted?

The children found a packing case and put it in the garden. They wrapped a hot water bottle in a blanket, and buried it under some straw. Then they got some fresh milk from the cow and gave it to Ben while it was still warm. They did this every three hours, day and night, until he started to look stronger. Then they stopped setting the alarm.

Ben was very quick and bright and loving, and soon became a pet. The children tried to wean him by giving him solid food, called creep, and Ben seemed to be able to take it.

He was looked after for three weeks, then he went back to the litter. His mother rejected him, but he survived the first week – and the next three – but at ten weeks old, he died.

1   Why do you think the children put a hot water bottle in his box?
2   Why did they stop setting the alarm?
3   Why do you think Mr Sharp put Ben back in the litter after three weeks?
4   What did Ben lose when his mother rejected him?
5   Why do you think Ben died?
6   Do you think the children did the right thing?

The next morning, on her way to see if there were any papers, Julie looked up at the sky, and saw what seemed to be a small grey patch in it. When she looked more carefully, she could see others. At the shop, Sam was staring upwards too.

'It's going to work! We'll see the sun again!' he said with joy.

By noon the sky looked like a grey paper doily. The holes were quite light, and getting larger.

The next day was the first for over two months that lights were switched off at mid-day.

How the clear cloud came to be formed was never known. A strange chemical reaction had taken place. Some said it was because of polluted air. Others said it came from space.

So far, it hasn't happened again.

1   Why do you think the first signs of the chemical working are grey patches?
2   Why do you think there might not have been papers?
3   What is so special about the sun that makes Sam so happy about seeing it again?
4   When does Spring come this year?
5   What could people do to try to prevent this happening again?
6   What lessons would a winter like this teach people?

Jimmy lay still at the bottom. Amy couldn't get to him as she wanted to do. Jimmy was taken away in an ambulance. Amy, shocked and upset, was surprised by Mike's reactions. He was pale and very quiet. He came to talk to her, a thing he'd never done before.

'Er, when you see Jimmy, wish him all the best from me, will you?' He moved away quickly, before she could do anything but nod.

Amy was Jimmy's first visitor. He was still suffering the effects of concussion.

'I kept seeing these coloured lights,' he murmured. 'And there was this deep humming noise. And I wanted to go home so much. I thought of you, and I didn't go this time ...' His voice tailed off.

'Thank you,' said Amy, and she gave him Mike's message.

1   What is surprising to Amy about Mike's reactions?
2   How do you explain Mike's reactions?
3   What do you think Jimmy is describing to Amy?
4   Why do you think Jimmy talks about it now?
5   If Jimmy had gone, how do you think it would have appeared to Amy?
6   What do you think Amy makes of what Jimmy says?